Introductory Guidanc
Insurance under JCT Contracts

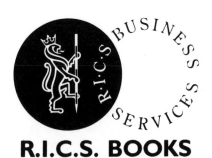

R.I.C.S. BOOKS

Published by Surveyors Holdings Limited
a wholly owned subsidiary of
The Royal Institution of Chartered Surveyors,
under the RICS Books imprint
12 Great George Street
London SW1P 3AD

A CIP catalogue record for this title is available from
the British Library.

ISBN 0 85406 488 5

CONTENTS

INTRODUCTION

The various standard forms of Building
Contracts, which have been published
over the years by the Joint Contracts
Tribunal, cover a range of building project
types from minor works carried out by a
jobbing contractor to multi-million pound
design and build projects.

In all projects, liability insurance is of
great importance and in view of the
complexity of the insurance requirements,
the insurance provisions in each of the
contracts other than MW80 are very
similar.

In order to understand the application and
operation of the insurance clauses, it is
necessary to have a basic understanding
of the nature of risk and liability to enable
the fairly complicated contract clauses to
be properly interpreted and applied.

The purpose of this introductory
Guidance Note is to outline the
philosophy behind insurance clauses
under JCT 80 and IFC 84 and indicate
how they deal with the various
eventualities.

The Guidance Note commences with a
consideration of the types of risk
encountered on a building contract, the
likely financial responsibilities and
liabilities and goes on to consider how
the insurance provisions address those
liabilities.

RISK, LIABILITY AND INSURANCE

1   SPECIFIED PERILS, EXCEPTED RISKS AND PERSONAL ACCIDENTS

During the course of a Building Contract many things can go wrong. Some of these events can relate to poor design or workmanship or relate to defective materials. Others however can be initially and collectively referred to as 'accidents' or events resulting in loss or damage.

The majority of these accidents or events fall into various categories:

1.1   Loss or damage caused by:
Fire, lightning, explosion, storm, tempest, flood, bursting or overflowing of water tanks apparatus or pipes, earthquakes, aircraft and other aerial devices or articles dropped therefrom, riot or civil commotion.
(In the context of JCT 80 and IFC 84 these are referred to as 'Specified Perils'.)

1.2   Loss or damage caused by:
(i)   any consequence of war, invasion, act of foreign enemy, hostilities (whether war be declared or not) civil war, rebellion, revolution, insurrection, military or usurped power, confiscation, commandeering, nationalisation or requisition or loss or destruction of or damage to any property by or under the order of any government public, municipal or local authority;
(ii)   any unlawful, wanton or malicious act committed maliciously by a person or persons acting on behalf of or in connection with an unlawful association.

1.3   Loss or damage caused by:
Ionising radiations or contamination by radioactivity from any nuclear fuel or from any nuclear waste from the combustion of nuclear fuel, radioactive, toxic, explosive or other hazardous properties of any explosive nuclear assembly or nuclear component thereof, pressure waves caused by aircraft or other aerial devices travelling at sonic or supersonic speeds.
(These are known as the 'Excepted Risks'.)

1.4   Personal accidents leading to death or injury.

2   DAMAGE OR LOSS TO PROPERTY

The events listed at 1.1 to 1.3 inclusive above may all lead to personal injury but are more likely to cause damage or loss to property, e.g.

2.1   To work which has been or is being carried out by a contractor or to materials on site and intended to be included in the works.

2.2   To the building in which works are being carried out, as in the case of a refurbishment or repair contract.

2.3   To the adjacent buildings belonging to the employer.

2.4   To adjacent buildings not belonging to the employer.

2.5   To property or possessions not belonging to the employer but nevertheless entitled to be there, e.g. tenants' personal effects in a building undergoing a repair.

2.6   To main services serving another property e.g. the breaking of a telephone cable.

3 FINANCIAL RESPONSIBILITY FOR DAMAGE OR LOSS TO PROPERTY

When loss or damage occurs, as in the situations outlined in 2.1-2.6 above, conflicts may arise as to which party must assume financial responsibility. Possible scenarios for each of the affected parties are as follows:

The Contractor

3.1 The works and/or materials which have been damaged may not have been paid for by the contractor's employer. To fulfill contractual obligations the contractor must carry out repairs but who will pay for the extra cost as the employer will only want to pay for it once?

3.2 The building in which the contractor's work is being carried out is damaged thus preventing the carrying out of the works until such time as the main building is reinstated by the employer. Who pays the cost resulting from this delay?

3.3 The works which have been damaged may have been paid for but who will pay the contractor to do it again, as in the absence of a promise to pay, the contractor may choose to repudiate the contract. Notwithstanding that, the Contractor could then become liable to the Employer for monetary compensation.

3.4 The building in which the works are being done is damaged, and the works are also damaged and may or may not have been paid for. Who will pay for the replacement or reinstatement of the building and/or the works?

The Adjoining Owner

3.5 Events on one site cause damage to an adjoining property held by a different owner. Who will pay for the repairs?

The Tenant

3.6 As a result of the works being done on the property occupied by a tenant, the tenant's possessions and/or property is damaged. How is the repair/replacement to be achieved?

4 NEGLIGENCE AND LIABILITY

4.1 The scenarios are endless but clearly the liability for bearing the cost of repair, whether to the works or to the building in which the work is taking place, will depend upon who is responsible for the event leading to loss or damage. This raises the question of negligence, e.g. was the fire caused by a careless electrician? The question of liability inherent in occupation is also raised, e.g. the contractor has possession of the site and therefore must be responsible for any damage that occurs there.

4.2 If a fast effective legal system and unlimited financial resources were available to the contractor, employer and adjoining owner and/or tenant, matters could be allowed to take their course. However, loss or damage to the works causes not only a reinstatement problem but also a problem of delay to the original contracted works. Protracted litigation over responsibility might result in a financial loss for delayed completion far in excess of the cost of reinstating the loss or damage to the works.

4.3 It has long been established, therefore, that the prudent contractor and employer insure the works and the buildings against as many risks as the insurance industry will allow, i.e. generally those referred to in paragraphs 1.1 and 1.4. In the past Standard Forms of Building Contract made provision for ensuring that appropriate policies were in existence so that most eventualities were covered. However, although these provisions dealt with the manner in which liability should be insured, delays often occurred while liability was being proved. Whilst the financial risks inherent in perpetrating a negligent act could be covered by insurance, the negligence still had to be proved.

4.4 The current JCT Forms of Contract, available since 1986, attempt to resolve the liability problem on issues affecting the progress of the works by including a requirement for Joint Names Policies by which the loss in question is dealt with *regardless of blame* thus minimising delay.

4.5 Before proceeding to the examination of the various insurance and liability clauses, a few general points are relevant.

4.5.1 Not all loss or damage is insurable. Loss or damage occasioned by the events listed in paragraph 1.3 — known as Excepted Risks is not insurable and the contractor is not responsible for any loss or damage brought about by those items.

4.5.2 All Risks Policies referred to later are not quite what they seem.

They do not cover the cost of repair or replacement due to:

(i) Wear and tear or obsolescence
(ii) Defective work or design or loss due to failure of supporting structure which failed due to defective workmanship or design.
(iii) The items listed in 1.2 above.
(iv) The items listed in 1.3 above.
(v) Civil commotion.

4.5.3 The events listed in paragraph 1.1 used to be referred to as 'Clause 22 Perils' in the context of JCT 80 — they are now referred to as 'Specified Perils'.

4.5.4 The following additional definitions may also be useful:

An Insurance Clause
A clause which describes the risks to be insured and the person who must arrange the insurance.

Risk Clause
A clause which allocates responsibility for risk,

> e.g. the existing structures together with the contents thereof shall be at the sole risks of the Employer as regards loss or damage by the Specified Perils.

Sometimes a clause is both a risk and an insurance clause.

Indemnity Clause
An indemnity clause is where one party agrees to compensate the other party to the contract in respect of loss or damage suffered by him.

Sole Risk
Sole risk means that the liability falls on one party to the contract alone with no right to recover from the other party to the contract, who may have caused the loss or damage. Thus if damage is caused to the employer's existing premises by the negligence of the contractor but the building contract provides that such damage shall be at the sole risk of the employer, the employer (or the employer's insurers) cannot recover from the negligent contractor.

Where the risk falls on one person (but not the sole risk) that person may attempt to recover the loss from the person at fault.

Subrogation
The right of the insurer, having paid a claim, to recover the payment from the person legally at fault.

Nominated Sub-Contractor
A sub-contractor who has been nominated by the contract administrator.

Domestic Sub-Contractor
A person to whom the contractor sub-lets any portion of the works other than a nominated sub-contractor. The contractor is not allowed to sub-let any portion of the works without the written consent of the contract administrator.

The Works
The works described in the building contract and shown and described in the contract drawings and in the contract bills/specification, including any changes made thereto in accordance with the contract.

Site Materials
All unfixed materials and goods delivered to, placed on or adjacent to the works and intended for incorporation therein.

Joint Names Policy
A policy of insurance, which may include amongst others, the contractor and the employer as the insured parties. If the contractor damages property owned by the employer, which is insured in their joint names, the insurer, having paid the employer, cannot recover the payment from the contractor; i.e. subrogation rights do not exist against joint insureds.

Practical Completion
The date on which the contract administrator certifies that the works are practically complete.

Excess
The first amount of any insurance claim which is not covered, e.g. if a policy has a £100 excess the insured is not paid for the first £100 of the claim.

Defects Liability and Making Good Defects
The contract administrator has to notify the contractor (not later than 14 days after the expiry of the defects liability period) of any defects, shrinkages or other faults which are due to materials or workmanship not in accordance with the contract or frost occurring before Practical Completion.

The contract administrator must issue a certificate (usually referred to as a certificate of Making Good Defects) to the contractor once the contractor has satisfactorily rectified all defects so notified.

INSURANCE UNDER JCT FORMS OF CONTRACT

Having considered potential conflicts and the necessity of providing for risk, liability and insurance within contracts it is appropriate to consider the current JCT Forms of Contract and the way in which these items are dealt with.

In November 1986 Amendments 1 & 2 were issued by the JCT setting out amendments to the Insurance and Related Liability Provisions applicable to the Intermediate Form of Contract (IFC) 1984 and the Standard Form of Building Contract 1980 respectively.

The main purpose of these amendments is to reflect current insurance practice and to remove some inconsistencies in the existing provisions. The following brief notes relate primarily to JCT 80 with margin notes indicating the equivalent clause under IFC 84.

It is stressed that the notes are not intended to be exhaustive, merely to indicate the general scope of a clause. A full appreciation of the meaning can only be gained by reading the clauses in their entirety.

It will be particularly noted that often the reference in the notes to contractor may also include sub-contractor in the actual clause. It should also be noted that under Clause 18.1.4 of the JCT 80 and Clause 2.1 of IFC 84 the obligation to insure generally only extends either to the date of Practical Completion or up to and including the date of determination of employment of the contractor (whether or not the validity of determination is contested), whichever is the sooner. A full appreciation of the reference to determination can only be gained by reference to the actual text of the clause.

INSURANCE UNDER JCT 80 AND IFC 84

JCT 80 Amendment 1 Clause		Equivalent IFC 84 Clause
Possession by Contractor — Use or occupation by Employer		
18.1.4	Deals with the question of insurance where the Employer takes early possession of all or part of the works thus affecting the contractor's responsibility and liabilities.	2.1
Injury to persons and property and indemnity of the Employer		
20.1	This is a risk and indemnity clause placing responsibility for personal injury resulting from the works upon the Contractor, other than where the injury results from negligence of the Employer.	6.1.1
20.2	This is a risk and indemnity clause placing responsibility for damage to property, due to negligence by the Contractor or persons for whom the Contractor is responsible, upon the Contractor.	6.1.2
20.3.1	Refers back to the property to which clause 20.2 relates, and excludes the Works and Materials from the definition of the property above, up to the date of the issue of the Certificate of Practical Completion as the insurance thereof is dealt with by Clause 22.	6.1.3
Insurance against injury to person or property		
21.1.1.1	Ensures that those liabilities imposed by clauses 20.1 and 20.2 are covered by insurance up to a sum, which has to be inserted in the Appendix, as the minimum sum to be insured.	6.2.1
21.1.2	Provides for the Employer to require evidence of insurance under 21.1.1.1 to be produced by the Contractor.	6.2.2
21.1.3	Provides for the Employer to insure where the Contractor defaults in insuring under 21.1.1.1 and to recover the premium from the Contractor.	6.2.3

JCT 80
Amendment 1
Clause

Equivalent
IFC 84
Clause

Insurance — liability of the Employer

21.2.1	Allows the Employer to require the Contractor to take out a Joint Names Policy, in a stated sum, to cover the Employer's liability for certain risks to property other than the Works and also to the Employer's own property. This clause also sets out certain exclusions.	6.2.4
	The clause goes on to give the Employer a right to approve the insurers, and also to have the policy and premium receipts deposited with him.	
	Any premiums are to be added to the Contract Sum i.e. they are paid by the Employer and in the Contractor's default in obtaining insurance, the Employer may insure.	
21.3	Removes the Contractor's liability or obligation to insure in respect of excepted risks.	6.2.5

Insurance of the Works

22.1	States that one of the three available clauses dealing with the insurance of the works i.e. 22A, 22B or 22C has to be selected and stated in the Appendix.	6.3.1
22.2	Sets out various definitions for use in interpreting clauses 22A, 22B or 22C.	6.3.1
22.3.1 and 22.3.2	Deal with the position of sub-contractors in relation to Joint Names Policies.	6.3.2

The 'Alternative Clauses'

Erection of New Buildings — All Risks Insurance of Works by Contractor

22A.1	Requires, if applied, the Contractor to take out a Joint Names All Risks Insurance for the cover defined in Clause 22.2.	6.3A.1

JCT 80
Amendment 1
Clause

Equivalent
IFC 84
Clause

JCT 80 Amendment 1 Clause		Equivalent IFC 84 Clause
22A.2	Notwithstanding that the insurance has to be taken out by the Contractor, this clause provides for the insurers to be approved by the Employer. It also allows for proof of insurance and proof of payment of premium to be provided to the Employer by the Contractor and for the Employer to arrange for such insurance in the Contractor's default, in which case the premiums are recovered from the Contractor.	6.3A.2
22A.3.1	Is an alternative clause to 22A.2. It provides for the Contractor, who has an annual policy covering risks defined in Clause 22.2, to add to this policy the Employer as a Joint Name in respect of the works to which the contract applies.	6.3A.3.1
22A.3.2	Applies the 'default' provisions of Clause 22A.2 to Clause 22A.3.1.	6.3A.3.2
22A.4.1	Places an obligation upon the Contractor to notify the Contract Administrator and Employer in writing when loss or damage has occurred.	6.3A.4.1
22A.4.2	States that when loss or damage has occurred, this shall be disregarded in computing amounts due to the Contractor. This means that valuations carried out after the damage has occurred, proceed as though nothing had happened — otherwise a negative valuation would occur and money become due from the Contractor to the Employer.	6.3A.4.2
22A.4.3	Requires the Contractor, following inspection by the Insurers, to make good the damage and complete the work.	6.3A.4.3
22A.4.4	Ensures that the Contractor, under the Joint Names Policy, authorises the insurers to pay monies due directly to the Employer, who then pays for the reinstatement work by instalments under the Contract Administrator's Certificates.	6.3A.4.4

JCT 80
Amendment 1
Clause

Equivalent
IFC 84
Clause

22A.4.5	States that the maximum amount that the Contractor can receive for the reinstatement works is that amount received under the insurance policy.	22A.4.5

Erection of New Buildings — All Risks Insurance of the Work by the Employer

22B.1 22B.2 22B.3.1 22B.3.2 22B.3.3 22B.3.4	Are similar to those under clause 22A but with the initiative for insurance being with the Employer rather than with the Contractor. Thus in the Employer's default the Contractor may insure and recover the premiums by having them added to the Contract Sum.	6.3B.1 6.3B.2 6.3B.3.1 6.3B.3.2 6.3B.3.3 6.3B.3.4
22B.3.5	Differs from 22A.4.4 and 22A.4.5 in that here the reinstatement work is dealt with and paid for as a variation to the contract with all that implies with regard to extensions of time, loss and expense claims etc. If the insurance monies are insufficient to cover the reinstatement work then the additional cost is borne by the Employer.	6.3B.3.5

Insurance of Existing Structures — Insurance of Works and Extensions to Existing Structures.

22C.1	Requires the Employer to take out a Joint Name Policy in respect of damage to the existing structures owned by the Employer and their contents arising from the Specified Perils, and for the Contractor, in the event of loss or damage, to authorise the insurers to pay all monies due to the Employer.	6.3C.1
22C.2	Requires the Employer to take out Joint Names All Risks Policy in respect of the Works.	6.3C.2

JCT 80 Amendment 1 Clause		Equivalent IFC 84 Clause
22C.3	Except where the Employer is a Local Authority * this clause requires the Employer to produce evidence of the insurance to the Contractor. In the event of a default, the Contractor may insure and recover the premiums by having them added to the Contract Sum. *Note* *The words 'Except where the Employer is a Local Authority' are not used in the Local Authority versions of JCT 80.	6.3A.4.5
22C.4	Obliges the Contractor to advise the Contract Administrator and the Employer in writing as soon as loss or damage covered by the Policy has occurred.	6.3C.4
22C.4.1	States, like Clause 22A.4.3 and 22B.3.2, that the loss or damage shall be disregarded when computing payments due to the Contractor under the contract.	6.3C.4.1
22C.4.2	Requires the Contractor to authorise the insurers to pay all monies due under the Joint Names Policy to the Employer.	6.3C.4.2
22C.4.3.1	Provides an opportunity for either party to the contract to determine the Contractor's employment following loss or damage, if it is just and equitable so to do, or to have the matter referred to an Arbitrator.	6.3C.4.3
22C.4.4	In the event of neither party opting to determine or the Arbitrator deciding against determination, this clause requires the Contractor to reinstate and for this work to be dealt with and paid for as a variation to the Contract. As in Clause 22B.3.5, if the insurance monies are insufficient then the Employer bears the additional cost.	6.3C.4.4

JCT 80
Amendment 1
Clause

Equivalent
IFC 84
Clause

Insurance for Employer's Loss of Liquidated & Ascertained Damages

22D.1	Clearly in the event of loss or damage occurring from a Specified Peril, the Contract Administrator may be obliged to grant an extension of time to deal with the delay, thus denying the Employer entitlement to liquidated and ascertained damages. This clause allows the Employer to recover this loss by requiring the Contractor to take out insurance.	6.3D.1
22D.2	States how the sum insured is to be calculated.	6.3D.2
22D.3	States how the payments under the policy shall be arrived at.	6.3D.3
22D.4	States that the premium paid by the Contractor shall be added to the Contract Sum and also provides for the Employer to insure in the event of the Contractor's default in so doing.	6.3D.4

INSURANCE UNDER THE AGREEMENT FOR MINOR BUILDING WORKS 1980 (MW80)

Under the Agreement for Minor Building Works 1980 (MW80) the insurance provisions are contained in Clause 6.

The matters dealt with are briefly as follows:

MW80
Clause

Injury to or death of persons

6.1   This is a risk, indemnity and insurance clause in relation to death or personal injury.

Injury or damage to property

6.2   Is an equivalent risk, indemnity and insurance clause which relates to damage to property other than that on which the Contractor is working or in which the work is being carried out. It states that the minimum amount of insurance cover required must be included in the contract. This requires careful consideration as the cover must be commensurate with the risk and could, at worst, have to cover the total cost of the reinstatement of all adjoining or adjacent buildings which might be damaged by the carrying out of works.

Insurance of the Works — Fire etc. — New Works

6.3A   Is a simplified version of the relevant part of clause 6.3 of IFC 84 suitable for the type of work for which MW80 should be used, as it only requires the works to be insured against the Specified Perils and not All Risks.

Insurance of the Works — Fire etc. — Existing Structures

6.3B   Is a simplified version of the relevant part of clause 6.3 of IFC 84 suitable for the type of work for which MW80 should be used, as it only requires the works to be insured against the Specified Perils and not All Risks.

MW80
Clause

Evidence of Insurance

6.4   Requires the Contractor and
             Employer, as appropriate, to provide
             reasonable evidence of insurance. It
             is to be noted that there is no
             provision for either party to insure in
             the other's default.

For those requiring further more detailed information reference should be made to Practice Note 22 and
Guide to the Amendments to the Insurance and Related Liability Provisions: 1986, published by the JCT.